SEARCH & FIND®

BLACK BEAUTY

by
Anna Sewell

Adapted by Jacqueline Ball
Illustrated by Tony Tallarico

A Kidsbooks® CLASSIC

Merrylegs

Black Beauty

Ginger

John Manly and
James Howard

Joe Green

Jerry Barker

TABLE OF CONTENTS

CHAPTER ONE
My First Home..6

CHAPTER TWO
My Training...8

CHAPTER THREE
Birtwick Park...10

CHAPTER FOUR
New Friends and a New Name...........................12

CHAPTER FIVE
Horses' Tales and Horses' Tails.......................14

CHAPTER SIX
"The River Is Rising!".....................................16

CHAPTER SEVEN
James Saves My Life......................................18

CHAPTER EIGHT
Riding for My Mistress's Life..........................20

CHAPTER NINE
Leaving Home..22

CHAPTER TEN
Earlshall Park..24

CHAPTER ELEVEN
Lady Anne...26

CHAPTER TWELVE
My Accident...28

CHAPTER THIRTEEN
A Cab Horse in London..................................30

CHAPTER FOURTEEN
Kind Customers and Happy Days......................32

CHAPTER FIFTEEN
My Poor Old Friend......................................34

CHAPTER SIXTEEN
An Unhappy New Year...................................36

CHAPTER SEVENTEEN
Hard Times..38

CHAPTER EIGHTEEN
Another Chance...40

CHAPTER NINETEEN
My Last Home..42

Quick Quiz..44

Activity Adventures.......................................45

About the Author..46

CHAPTER ONE

My First Home

When I was a young colt, I lived in a beautiful meadow. I remember a clear pond and shady trees. There was a field on one side. My master's house was on the other side.

SEARCH & FIND®

Squirrels (2)
Fish (3)
Flowers (3)
Kite
Carrots (3)
Bucket
Heart
Birds (4)
Mice (2)
Mushrooms (3)
Green apple
Tree stump
Top hat
Owl
Rope
Anchor
Umbrella
Worm
Artist's brush
Turtle

Back then, I lived on my mother's milk. I always stayed by her side.

When I was old enough to eat grass, my mother had to go back to work during the day. I played with the older colts. Sometimes our play was rough.

One day my mother saw us and called me over. She said, "Never bite or kick, even in play. I want you to grow up gentle and never learn bad ways."

CHAPTER TWO

My Training

A s I grew up, I heard people call me handsome. I had a bright black coat, one white foot, and a star on my forehead. When I was four, it was time to be sold.

SEARCH & FIND®

Pitchfork
Envelope
Candy cane
Flowers (2)
Hammer
Rope
Mice (2)
Lost boot
Carrots (2)
Nail
Snake
Spoon
Birds (2)
Quarter moons (2)
Ring
Toothbrush
Horseshoes (2)
Green apple
Bell
Butterfly

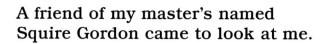
A friend of my master's named Squire Gordon came to look at me.

HE'S A FINE ONE! WHO WILL BREAK HIM IN?

I WILL DO IT MYSELF. I DON'T WANT HIM FRIGHTENED OR HURT.

To break in a horse means to teach him or her to wear a saddle, respond to a bit, and get used to other uncomfortable things. It means teaching a horse to pull a carriage and to know when the master wants to go fast or slow.

My master knew that breaking me in would be no fun for a high-spirited colt like me. Before we started, he gave me a treat.

HERE, SMOKY, SOME NICE OATS.

The oats tasted good. But then he gently put a piece of cold steel into my mouth. That was the bit. It tasted nasty! He slid the bridle over my head, talking kindly.

EASY DOES IT. IT'S ALL RIGHT.

He saddled me up and rode me around the meadow. Carrying someone on my back felt strange at first.

The blacksmith nailed iron shoes to my feet. It didn't hurt, but the shoes made my feet feel heavy.

In time I got used to everything that grown-up horses have to wear for work.

For my last part of training, I stayed in a field near a railroad track. The loud whistle scared me at first, but I got used to it. My master would often need me to get him to the train station. He didn't want me to be frightened by the noise.

I practiced pulling a carriage with my mother. Our master knew she could teach me better than a strange horse could.

My mother knew I would be leaving soon. She told me that the better I behaved, the better I would be treated. Then she said, "Some owners are kind and others are cruel. Some are foolish. I hope you fall into good hands, my dear."

CHAPTER THREE

Birtwick Park

One day a man came to take me to Squire Gordon's home. It was a place called Birtwick Park.

SEARCH & FIND®

Screwdriver
Artist's brushes (2)
Fish
Bird
Stars (2)
Buckets (2)
Umbrella
Knife
Arrows (2)
Hearts (2)
Toothbrush
Fork
Mushrooms (2)
Shark fin
Whip
Hammer
Pencil
Top hat
Barrels (2)

A fat little gray pony was in the next stall. I introduced myself. "My name is Merrylegs," he told me. "The children like to ride me. I hope you don't bite."

"The only things I bite are hay and oats," I told Merrylegs.

Then I heard an angry voice. "So it is you who has turned a lady out of her home!" It was a chestnut mare.

"I was put here," I protested. "I didn't mean to take your place." But the mare jerked her head away.

Merrylegs told me that the mare's name was Ginger. "She bit a groom, so they took her out of the loose box. She says she acts badly because she has been treated badly in the past. But people are kind here."

CHAPTER FOUR

New Friends and a New Name

 fter a few days Ginger became friendlier. The people at Birtwick Park were friendly right away. I really liked the coachman, John Manly.

SEARCH & FIND®

Carrot
Horseshoes (2)
Flowers (3)
Green apple
Bone
Guitar
Brushes (2)
Saws (2)
Key
Heart
Buckets (2)
Kites (2)
Skull
Stool
Volcano
Quarter moon
Frying pan
Balloon
Pumpkin
Sailboat

One morning John took me for a ride. At first we rode slowly; then we went faster and faster.

YOU'RE A GOOD ONE!

On our way back we met the Squire Gordon and his wife.

HE'S FIRST-RATE, SIR! FAST AS A DEER, YET EASILY GUIDED.

EXCELLENT! I'LL TRY HIM MYSELF TOMORROW.

The next day, Mrs. Gordon was waiting when we finished our ride.

HE IS ALL THAT JOHN SAID HE WAS. WHAT SHOULD WE CALL HIM?

HE IS QUITE A BEAUTY. WHAT ABOUT BLACK BEAUTY?

Now I had a new name and kind new friends. Besides John Manly, a boy named James Howard worked in the stable. He liked to brush me until my coat was glossy.

YOUR MANE WILL BE SOFT AS A FINE LADY'S HAIR, MY BEAUTY!

Ginger and I often pulled the carriage together. We became even closer friends.

THESE TWO HORSES KEEP IN PERFECT STEP!

IT'S AS IF THEY WERE COMMUNICATING WITH EACH OTHER.

I was happy in my new home, but sometimes I missed my freedom. I felt restless and would jump around my stall. Some grooms would punish a horse for that, but John knew just what I needed.

A GOOD RUN WILL WORK OUT THOSE JITTERS!

John was as kind as my first master. I told Ginger how my master had patiently broken me in. "Well," she said, "no wonder you have such a good temperament. That's not how it was for me."

"Some men forced the bit into my mouth. It hurt. I was so scared."

"Later, my master's son set out to break my spirit. He ran me around the field until I was so tired that I could hardly stand."

"He whipped me, too. One day I couldn't take it anymore. I threw him off. Then I ran to a pasture. I stood there all day with nothing to eat or drink."

"My old master found me. He patted me and led me to the barn. His son stayed away while the master broke me in himself. He was kind, but others were cruel."

POOR, POOR GIRL!

CHAPTER FIVE

Horses' Tales and Horses' Tails

inger had been through terrible times, but she became more cheerful with the kind treatment at Birtwick Hall. Meanwhile, the other horses had their own tales to tell.

SEARCH & FIND®

Hazel sticks (2)
Orange
Flowers (3)
Coffeepot
Green apple
Carrot
Pear
Mushrooms (3)
Fish
Horseshoes (2)
Screwdriver
Rabbit
Birds (2)
Snake
Worm
Paintbrush
Knife
Saw
Umbrella
Hammer

One day the minister brought his children to visit. Merrylegs was taken out so the children could ride him. Later James brought the pony back. He spoke sternly.

YOU MUST BEHAVE BETTER OR WE'LL ALL BE IN TROUBLE!

I asked Merrylegs what happened. "The young ladies rode me for two hours, and then one of the boys wanted his turn. He cut a big whip from a hazel stick and hit me with it."

"I stopped suddenly a few times to warn him, but he kept hitting me. So I just rose up and let him slip off."

"You should have kicked him!" cried Ginger. "No," Merrylegs replied. "My master trusts me. If I took to kicking, I could be sold to a place where no one cared for me. I love it here. I want to stay."

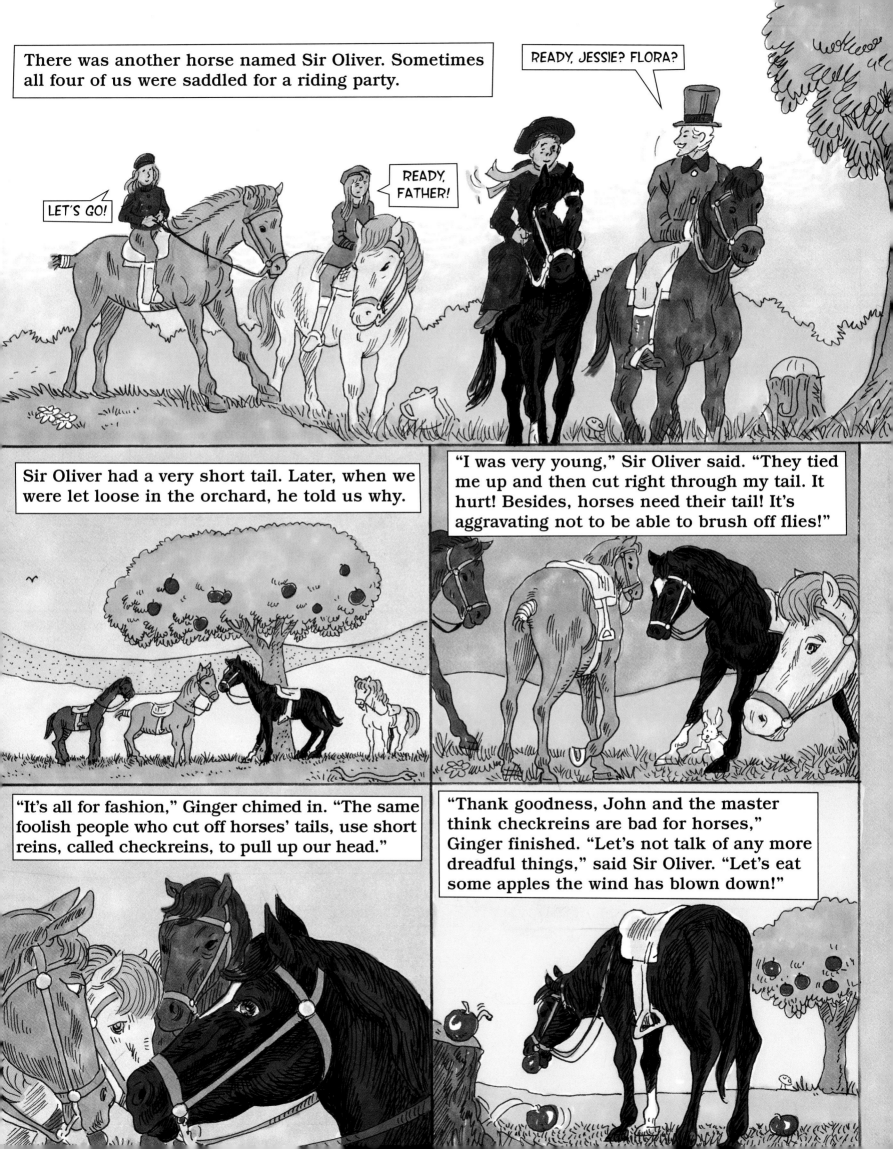

CHAPTER SIX

"The River Is Rising!"

One fall day Squire Gordon had some business in another town. John hitched me to a cart, and he and the master and I drove off. It had rained a lot. The wind blew hard.

SEARCH & FIND®

Lanterns (2)
Deer
Fish (2)
Snake
Cane
Arrows (2)
Paintbrush
Hammer
Coffeepot
Falling leaf
Birds (2)
Flowers (2)
Soccer ball
Owls (2)
Suitcase
Hearts (3)
Horseshoe
Skull
Apples (2)
Snail

CHAPTER SEVEN

James Saves My Life

That night I enjoyed a special supper and then fell right to sleep. I was very tired from our adventure. I didn't know that another adventure would happen soon.

SEARCH & FIND®

Pipe

Corncob

Flowers (2)

Hammer

Buckets (3)

Heart

Umbrellas (2)

Bone

Knife

Fish

Mice (2)

Mailbox

Paintbrushes (2)

Horseshoes (2)

Bottle

Ropes (5)

Bird

Barrels (3)

Lost boot

Skulls (2)

Toothbrush

A few days later the master came to speak with John.

JOHN, WHAT DO YOU THINK OF JAMES?

HE'S A SMART, HONEST YOUNG FELLOW.

MY BROTHER-IN-LAW NEEDS A COACHMAN. WOULD YOU RECOMMEND JAMES?

OF COURSE! BUT WE SHALL MISS HIM.

James was pleased at the job offer, but sad to leave his friends and family.

WHEN SHALL I GO, SIR?

IN A FEW WEEKS.

James spent the time practicing how to drive the carriage with Ginger and me. One day we drove the master and mistress to visit friends in another town.

We dropped them at an inn. James left us at a stable, then went to get some rest.

Later, I saw a new horse being led in. One groom rubbed him down while the other smoked a pipe. I knew John did not allow pipes in Birtwick Hall's stables.

I'M ABOUT DONE. GIVE THE HORSES FRESH HAY BEFORE YOU GO, WOULD YOU?

SURE THING.

CHAPTER EIGHT

Riding for My Mistress's Life

Ginger told me later that she heard me whinny while the stable was burning. She said it gave her the courage to go with James. But his calm actions were really what saved us. Two other horses did not survive the fire.

SEARCH & FIND®

Artist's brushes (2)

Arrow

Bell

Snake

Kites (2)

Envelopes (2)

Buckets (3)

Apple

Key

Horseshoe

Worm

Oilcan

Rabbit

Quarter moons (2)

Wagon wheel

Candle

Locomotive

Turtles (2)

Anchor

Heart

At Birtwick Park, John praised James for his courage. Then they talked about the future.

WHO WILL LOOK AFTER THE HORSES WHEN I'M GONE, JOHN?

THAT CHILD?

LITTLE JOE GREEN.

HE'S FOURTEEN. HE IS SMALL, BUT QUICK AND WILLING. AND HE HAS A KIND HEART.

The next day, young Joe Green came to the stables. He groomed Merrylegs while James watched.

At first Merrylegs complained about being groomed by a child. But soon he had to admit that Joe learned fast. Finally the day came for James to leave. His voice sounded so sad.

I SHALL MISS ALL MY FRIENDS, AND THE HORSES I LOVE SO MUCH.

AND WE SHALL ALL MISS YOU, JAMES.

A few days later, I was awakened by the stable bell. John was in my stall.

WAKE UP, BEAUTY! WE MUST RIDE FASTER THAN EVER TONIGHT.

The master was waiting at his front door. He held out an envelope.

BRING THIS NOTE TO DOCTOR WHITE. GIVE BEAUTY A REST BEFORE RETURNING, IF YOU CAN.

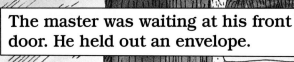

YES, SIR.

CHAPTER NINE

Leaving Home

John stayed angry at Joe for a long time. He told the master that ignorance was no excuse for almost killing me. Poor Joe was sick with guilt. But he would soon have a chance to show his true worth.

SEARCH & FIND®

Nail
Bucket
Hammer
Broom
Hearts (2)
Broken hearts (2)
Pencil
Kite
Umbrella
Bow
Candle
Birdhouses (2)
Fish
Mice (2)
Spears (2)
Rings (2)
Book
Horseshoe
Drum
Sword

One day Joe and I were coming home from an errand. We passed a cart loaded with bricks and stuck in the mud. Two horses were trying to pull it out. The driver was whipping them.

Joe and I were both angry. We proceeded to the house of Mr. Clay, the master brick-maker. Joe told Mr. Clay what he had seen.

At home, Joe told John what happened. I could tell that John's opinion of Joe rose instantly.

Later Joe testified against the man. We heard that the man might have to go to prison. After that, Joe seemed different. He was so proud of himself for doing the right thing that he seemed to grow inches taller.

I had lived in my happy home for three years when sad news came. Our mistress was still very ill. Doctors told her she must move to a warmer country. She and the master were breaking up the household and leaving England.

Merrylegs was given to the minister. Joe Green would go along as the groom. Sir Oliver had a new home, too, and Ginger and I were sold to an earl. John Manly was going to work as a colt breaker.

On our last morning together, Ginger and I brought the carriage to the master's door.

At the station, we waited while John took the master and mistress inside. Soon the train came puffing into sight and took them away. We drove slowly back to Birtwick Park for the last time.

CHAPTER TEN

Earlshall Park

In the morning, John hitched Ginger and me to the carriage. We moved on to our new home. It was called Earlshall Park.

SEARCH & FIND®

Bottle

Squirrel

Umbrella

Fish

Bells (2)

Candle

Feathers (2)

Coffeepot

Horseshoes (4)

Seal

Flowers (2)

Cup

Envelope

Bow and arrow

Keys (2)

Mushrooms (2)

Pen

Spoon

Birds (2)

Music note

Our new coachman's name was Mr. York.

TELL ME ABOUT THE HORSES.

THE BLACK ONE HAS A PERFECT TEMPERAMENT. THE MARE USUALLY BEHAVES WELL, BUT SHE ACTS UP NOW AND THEN. WE THINK SHE WAS BADLY TREATED ONCE.

THAT IS GOOD TO KNOW.

Then I heard something alarming.

YOU SHOULD ALSO KNOW THAT THESE HORSES HAVE NOT WORN CHECKREINS.

OUR MISTRESS WANTS HER HORSES REINED TIGHTLY. SHE LIKES THEM TO HOLD THEIR HEADS HIGH. IT'S THE FASHION.

I'M SORRY TO HEAR THAT.

I didn't have much time to worry about checkreins, because John was saying goodbye. I would never see him again.

GOODBYE, MY BEAUTY. GOOD LUCK.

The next day the earl came to look at us. He seemed very pleased. York told him what John had said about us.

I SEE. WELL, TIGHTEN THE CHECKREIN A LITTLE AT A TIME.

YES, SIR.

Later we were hitched to the carriage. We had to wear the checkrein, but it didn't seem very tight. The mistress frowned at us but said nothing.

CHAPTER ELEVEN

Lady Anne

At least there was one kind person at Earlshall Park. She was Lady Anne, one of the earl's daughters. In the spring, Lady Anne stayed home while her mother and father took a long trip. The earl's friend, Colonel Blantyre, was staying there, too.

SEARCH & FIND®

Pink ribbons (3)

Stars (3)

Owls (2)

Bottle

Brushes (2)

Shovel

Music note

Drum

Log

Pick

Bucket

Birds (2)

Snake

Pencil

Snails (2)

Envelope

Umbrella

Axe

Can

Apple

Turtle

Lady Anne liked to ride me. She named me Black Auster.

AUSTER MEANS SOUTH WIND. IT'S PERFECT FOR YOU BECAUSE YOU RUN SO FAST.

Colonel Blantyre's favorite horse was a mare named Lizzie. One day on a shopping trip Lady Anne wanted to switch horses, just for fun.

I'LL ONLY BE IN THE SHOP A MINUTE.

WE'LL WAIT HERE.

Some colts came trotting by. A boy behind them cracked a whip. One colt bolted across the road and smashed into Lizzie. She raced away with Anne.

I neighed and Blantyre ran outside. He untied my reins and we raced after Lizzie. She was running across a large field covered with bushes. I knew the ground was uneven.

THEY WENT THAT WAY!

STOP THEM BEFORE THE LADY IS KILLED!

CHAPTER TWELVE

My Accident

But a happy life was not to be. A few days later, the head groom hitched me to a carriage and drove to town. The groom's name was Reuben Smith. We left the carriage for repairs, and then Reuben went to a tavern. I was left with a hostler, a man who takes care of horses.

SEARCH & FIND®

Rabbit
Star
Corncob
Fish (3)
Carrots (2)
Worms (2)
Knife
Broken hammer
Mouse
Horseshoe
Owl
Artist's brushes (2)
Lanterns (2)
Yellow apple
Red flower
Spilled bucket
Arrows (3)
Spiderweb
Snail
Dog

Reuben was gone for hours. When he returned, the hostler told him that I had a loose shoe.

YOU SHOULDN'T RIDE THE HORSE THAT WAY. HE COULD TAKE A FALL!

AH, HE'LL BE ALL RIGHT.

Reuben's voice sounded rough and mean. He made me run fast over the stony road. My shoe became looser, then fell off. The sharp stones cut all the way into my foot. The pain was terrible. I stumbled and fell on my knees. Reuben was flung off.

Reuben lay still. I hobbled to the side of the road. Hours later, men from Earlshall Park came by.

IT'S REUBEN SMITH. HE'S DEAD!

LOOK, THE HORSE HAS LOST A SHOE. HIS FOOT IS CUT TO PIECES!

Later, the tavern keeper and the hostler told police that Reuben had been drunk. The accident was not my fault. A doctor treated my wounds.

WHAT A SHAME! THESE KNEES WILL NEVER BE THE SAME.

My knees healed, but they were scarred. The earl was very upset when he returned from London.

IT'S A PITY, YORK, BUT THIS HORSE IS RUINED. I CAN'T HAVE THOSE KNEES IN MY STABLE.

I HAVE A FRIEND WITH A CARRIAGE-RENTAL BUSINESS. HE MAY WANT TO TAKE BLACK AUSTER.

CHAPTER THIRTEEN

A Cab Horse in London

Mr. Barry hired a salesman to sell me at a horse fair. There were all kinds of horses there. Some were splendid young animals that had been treated well. Others were broken down.

SEARCH & FIND®

A	N
B	O
C	P
D	Q
E	R
F	S
G	T
H	U
I	V
J	W
K	X
L	Y
M	Z

There were all kinds of people there, too. I tried to look and act my best so someone nice would buy me.

THIS ONE LOOKS LIKE A WINNER.

YES, SIR. PLENTY OF BREEDING THERE.

ABOUT SIX YEARS OLD, I'D SAY, BY HIS TEETH.

But most of the buyers turned away when they saw my scarred knees.

A HORSE WITH KNEES LIKE THAT MIGHT FALL AGAIN.

A cheerful-looking man examined me gently and patted me. He offered some money, but the salesman said it wasn't enough. The man went away – then he came back!

HERE. I'LL PAY YOUR PRICE.

HE'S ALL YOURS.

My new owner rode me into London. He waved to the drivers at a cabstand.

HELLO, BOYS!

HELLO, JERRY! I SEE YOU FOUND A REPLACEMENT FOR JACK.

HE LOOKS LIKE A FINE FELLOW.

YES, INDEED!

CHAPTER FOURTEEN

Kind Customers and Happy Days!

P olly was right. Everything did work out. One night she met Jerry at the door with very good news.

SEARCH & FIND®

Vase
Pencils (2)
Hearts (2)
Falling leaf
Birds (2)
Barrels (3)
Slice of bread
Shovel
Butterfly
Lost boot
Black cat
Lost glove
Teapots (2)
Yo-yo
Ring
Worm
Apples (3)
Toothbrush
Bell
Apple core

Mrs. Briggs's servant had stopped by the house that afternoon with a request.

JERRY, MRS. BRIGGS WANTS YOU TO TAKE HER OUT TOMORROW AT 11 O'CLOCK!

THEY DIDN'T LIKE HIM AS WELL AS YOU!

BUT I THOUGHT THEY HAD FOUND ANOTHER DRIVER.

One Sunday, Jerry and I *did* work. We brought a neighbor to visit her sick mother in the country. While we waited, we relaxed in a meadow.

When we came home in the late afternoon, Polly had dinner waiting.

JACK AND I WORKED, BUT WE RELAXED, TOO. AND I PICKED SOME FLOWERS FOR YOU.

OH!

CHAPTER FIFTEEN

My Poor Old Friend

O ne day, a shabby old cab drove up to our stand. The horse was a worn-out chestnut mare. She was so skinny her bones showed through her coat. I looked at her with pity.

SEARCH & FIND

Walking cane
Candy cane
Dented hat
Broken windows (2)
Paintbrushes (2)
Flowers (2)
Lamppost
Lost sock
Knife
Fish (2)
Banana peel
Flying bat
Candles (2)
Worm
Arrow
Buckets (2)
Apple core
Newspaper
Barrels (2)
Sack

She saw me looking and called, "Black Beauty, is that you?" It was Ginger!

Her neck and legs were very thin. Her face was full of pain instead of its old pride. She was wheezing. I took a few steps closer so I could hear her sad story.

"I was ridden so hard as a hunting horse that I became short of breath," she told me. "I was sold again and again. At last I was bought by a cab company. The drivers whip me and I never get even one day of rest."

I felt so sorry for her. "You used to stand up for yourself, Ginger," I said. "Don't you kick and bite when you're treated badly?"

"It doesn't do any good," she said sadly. "If people are cruel, animals can't change them. People have all the power in this world."

COME ON! OUR PASSENGER IS IN A HURRY.

CHAPTER SIXTEEN

An Unhappy New Year

I got used to our busy life in London. Every day I liked Jerry more. He was considerate and caring, even if it meant he lost money.

SEARCH & FIND®

Drumstick
Hourglasses (2)
Lanterns (2)
Bird cage
Red crosses (3)
Fish
Bird
Oar
Book
Ropes (2)
Flower
Mouse
Golf clubs (2)
Horseshoe
Barrel
Stool
Candle
Quarter moons (2)
Heart
Axe

One morning, a young woman came running up to our stand. She was carrying a baby.

WHERE IS THE HOSPITAL? MY CHILD IS VERY SICK.

BUT I DON'T HAVE ANY MONEY!

I'LL TAKE YOU, MISS.

DON'T WORRY.

Just then, two well-dressed men jumped into the cab.

SORRY, SIRS. THIS LADY WAS HERE FIRST.

HER NEEDS ARE MORE IMPORTANT TO ME THAN YOUR MONEY.

LADY? WE HAVE IMPORTANT BUSINESS! AND WE CAN PAY YOU A LOT MORE!

The angry men finally got out. We drove fast to the hospital.

I'LL COME INSIDE WITH YOU.

YOU ARE SO KIND.

When Jerry came out, a lady called his name.

JEREMIAH BARKER! I'M SO GLAD TO SEE YOU AGAIN! CAN YOU TAKE ME TO PADDINGTON STATION?

I'D BE HONORED, MA'AM.

The lady had been Polly's employer. She told Jerry that she would hire him if he ever wanted to stop driving a cab.

HERE IS MONEY FOR THE RIDE. AND THIS IS FOR YOUR DEAR CHILDREN.

THANK YOU!

CHAPTER SEVENTEEN

Hard Times

Jerry got better, but the doctor said he could never go back to cab work. I knew the family was worried about money. One morning Dolly ran into the stable.

SEARCH & FIND®

Yellow bonnets (3)

Artist's brush

Ice-cream cone

Flowers (3)

Eyeglasses (3)

Barrel

Skull

Dog

Pencil

Flowerpot

Book

Viking helmet

Ice skates (2)

Stars (2)

Music note

Telescope

Whips (4)

Anchor

Arrow

Ring

CHAPTER EIGHTEEN

Another Chance

I lay there as the luggage was taken down and the family left. I heard a policeman giving orders, but I did not even open my eyes. Someone kindly gave me a drink and covered me with a blanket. When I could finally get up, I was led to a nearby stable.

SEARCH & FIND®

Screwdrivers (2)

Fishing pole

Carrots (4)

Bucket

Lock

Flowers (2)

Dart

Fish

Birds (5)

Rabbits (2)

Key

Horseshoes (3)

Bone

Oilcan

Kite

Owl

Saws (2)

Mushrooms (2)

Candle

Cup

A doctor looked me over. The driver stood by, scowling.

THIS HORSE WILL NEVER BE GOOD FOR CAB WORK AGAIN.

NURSE HIM FOR A COUPLE OF WEEKS UNTIL HE'S WELL ENOUGH TO SELL.

SO THE COMPANY WILL LOSE THE MONEY WE PAID?

So, soon I was at another horse sale. My spirit and energy were all used up. I didn't care who bought me – until I heard a nice-looking farmer and a boy talking about me.

THAT HORSE HAS KNOWN BETTER DAYS, WILLIE.

POOR OLD FELLOW! DO YOU THINK HE WAS EVER A CARRIAGE HORSE?

HE COULD HAVE BEEN ANYTHING.

The farmer patted my neck. I put my nose against him and nudged him.

LOOK HOW HE UNDERSTANDS KINDNESS, GRANDPA! I'LL BET WE COULD MAKE HIM HEALTHY AGAIN AT THE FARM!

I'M AFRAID HE MAY BE TOO OLD TO RECOVER.

I DON'T THINK HE IS SO OLD.

The salesman walked over.

THE BOY IS RIGHT. THIS HORSE ISN'T SO OLD. HE'S JUST WORN OUT FROM TOO MUCH WORK.

CHAPTER NINETEEN

My Last Home

One day, the groom cleaned me so carefully that I knew something special was going to happen. Willie and his grandfather hitched me to the buggy.

SEARCH & FIND®

Towel
Star
Carrot
Bonnet
Horseshoes (2)
Eyeglasses (3)
Bird
Owls (2)
Hammers (2)
Arrows (2)
Quarter moons (2)
Broom
Jugs (2)
Pencils (2)
Buckets (2)
Apples (10)
Hearts (2)
Umbrella
Coffeepot
Rabbit

We rode to a pretty house with flowers in front.

IF THE SISTERS LIKE HIM, HE'LL HAVE A GOOD HOME.

HOW CAN THEY HELP BUT LIKE HIM?

Willie jumped out and rang the doorbell. A housekeeper opened the door.

YES?

MY GRANDFATHER WOULD LIKE TO TALK TO THE LADIES, MA'AM.

Mr. Thoroughgood went inside. Shortly he came back with three ladies. They all looked at me and asked questions. One was worried about my scarred knees.

HE'S OBVIOUSLY HAD ONE BAD FALL. WILL HE FALL DOWN AGAIN?

THAT WOULD GIVE ME A TERRIBLE FRIGHT.

Mr. Thoroughgood said he was sure my injury wasn't my fault.

TRY HIM FOR A FEW DAYS. IF YOU DON'T FEEL HE IS PERFECTLY SAFE, I'LL TAKE HIM BACK.

YOUR GOOD WORD MEANS A LOT TO US.

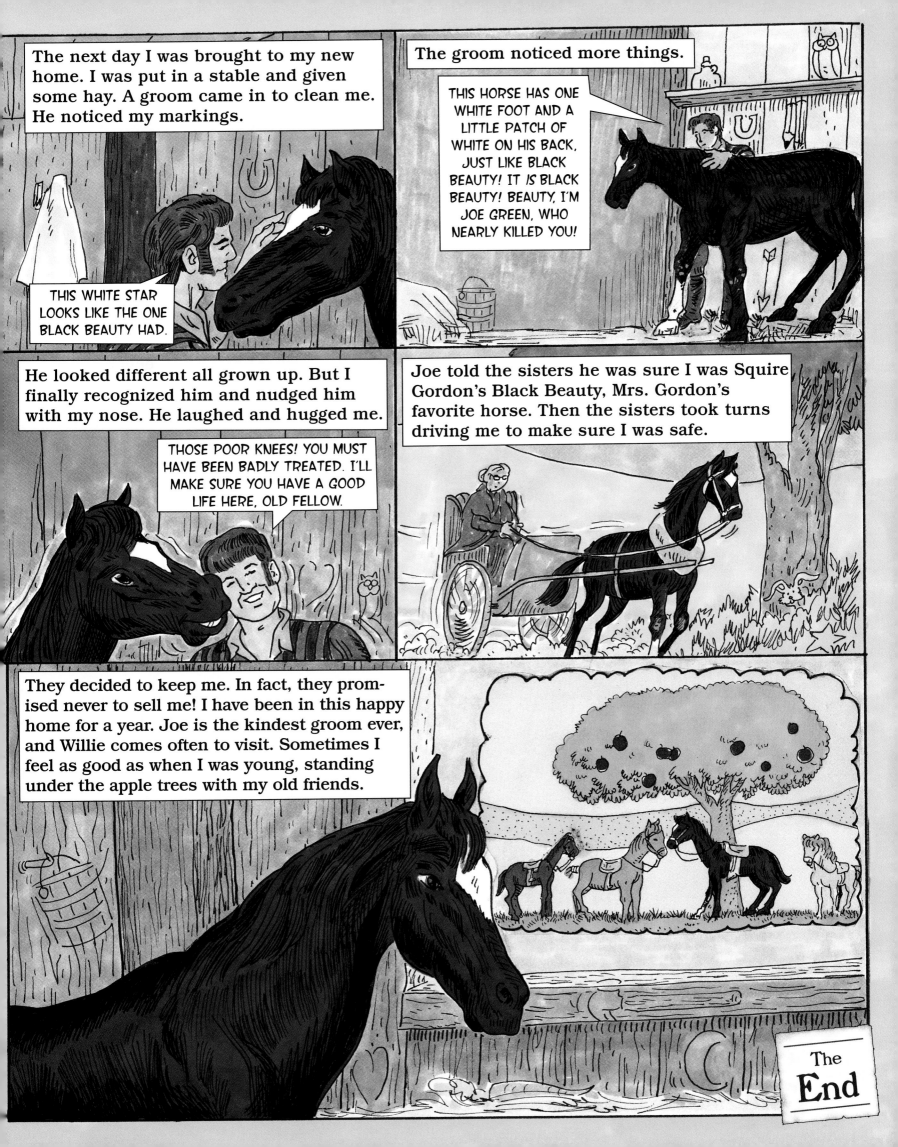

Quick Quiz

Check your answers on page 45.

1 *Black Beauty* is primarily about the main character's search for and wish for what?
    a. buried treasure
    b. kindness
    c. food and shelter
    d. his mother

2 When Black Beauty is a colt, what does his mother say that she wants him to do?
    a. grow up gentle and never learn bad ways
    b. become a winning racehorse, no matter what
    c. learn to defend himself by kicking and biting
    d. run away and become a wild horse

3 Which word best describes Black Beauty's treatment when he was a colt?
    a. strange
    b. cruel
    c. exotic
    d. kind

4 Why does Ginger tend to bite and snap?
    a. She was treated badly when she was younger.
    b. She just doesn't like people.
    c. She can't control herself.
    d. Her bit hurts.

5 How does Ginger's behavior change after a few days at Birtwick Park?
    a. She remains as mean as ever.
    b. She becomes more gentle.
    c. She begins to mope all the time.
    d. Her behavior stays the same.

6 Which piece of equipment do the horses think is cruel?
    a. saddles
    b. halters
    c. checkreins
    d. bits

7 What does James's behavior during the stable fire show?
    a. that he fears fire
    b. that the horses trust him
    c. that he knows the layout of the stables very well
    d. that he is able to break in horses quickly

8 Why does Black Beauty get sick after his long run to get the doctor?
    a. Joe Green gives him cold water and leaves him uncovered.
    b. He catches an infection from the mistress.
    c. Joe Green makes him run even farther.
    d. John accidentally leaves the stable door open and Black Beauty catches cold.

9 Why does Black Beauty leave Birtwick Park?
    a. He behaves badly, so his master sells him.
    b. The family has to leave England because of his mistress's health.
    c. Birtwick Park bans horses.
    d. He gets too old.

10 How does Jerry Barker use Black Beauty?
    a. to pull his cab
    b. to plow his fields
    c. to deliver bricks
    d. to entertain his guests

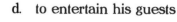

Activity Adventures

Black Beauty Today

Black Beauty's story takes place more than one hundred years ago, when cabs and carriages were pulled by horses. Today, we have engines to do those jobs. On a separate piece of paper, respond to the following:

- What jobs do horses still do today?
- Describe ways in which we use horses for sports or entertainment.
- What kind of life do you think these horses lead?

Kindness Comes First

When they move to Earlshall Park, Black Beauty and Ginger are forced to wear painful checkreins. They have no one to stick up for them. On a separate piece of paper, write a letter to the mistress of Earlshall Park explaining why she should no longer use checkreins. Suggest better ways she could treat her animals.

Extra, Extra—Read All About It!

Imagine that you are a writer for a horse magazine and wish to write about Black Beauty. Think about all of his adventures, and write a title for as many as you can. Use a separate piece of paper for each. Then draw pictures to go with each title. Here are a few to get started:

- Horse Falls Pulling Heavy Load
- Bridge Collapses; Horse Is Hero
- Fast Horse Saves Mistress

About the Author

Anna Sewell

Anna Sewell was born in 1820 in Yarmouth, England. Her parents were Quakers. They worked hard to make conditions better for the poor and needy. Anna's mother was also a best-selling author. Her father was a businessman.

When she was 15, Anna sprained both ankles in an accident. Her legs never fully recovered, and she was never able to walk well again. She got around on horseback or in a horse cart. Because of this, she became very fond of horses.

Anna Sewell's *Black Beauty* shows how much she knew about and loved horses. The book was published only a few months before she died in 1878. It was read by many people. It made them aware of how badly some horses were treated, and it led to new laws protecting animals. Anna Sewell was buried in a Quaker cemetery in Boston, England.